ALIENS
AND ENERGY

WRITTEN BY AGNIESZKA BISKUP · ILLUSTRATED BY AÓN

Raintree

GRAPHIC LIBRARY

Essex County Council

3013020336 95 4

www.raintreepublishers.co.uk
Visit our website to find out
more information about
Raintree books.

To order:
☎ Phone 0845 6044371
📄 Fax +44 (0) 1865 312263
💻 Email myorders@raintreepublishers.co.uk

Customers from outside the UK please telephone +44 1865 312262

Raintree is an imprint of Capstone Global Library Limited, a company incorporated
in England and Wales having its registered office at 7 Pilgrim Street, London,
EC4V 6LB – Registered company number: 6695582.

Text © 2012 Capstone Press
First published by Capstone Press in 2012
First published in the United Kingdom by Capstone Global Library in 2012
The moral rights of the proprietor have been asserted.

All rights reserved. No part of this publication may be reproduced in any
form or by any means (including photocopying or storing it in any medium by
electronic means and whether or not transiently or incidentally to some other use of this
publication) without the written permission of the copyright owner, except in accordance
with the provisions of the Copyright, Designs and Patents Act 1988 or under the terms of
a licence issued by the Copyright Licensing Agency, 6–10 Kirby Street, London EC1N 8TS
(www.cla.co.uk). Applications for the copyright owner's written permission should be
addressed to the publisher.

Editors: Anthony Wacholtz and Diyan Leake
Art Director: Nathan Gossman
Designer: Lori Bye
Originated by Capstone Global Library Ltd
Printed and bound in China by South China Printing Company Ltd

ISBN 978 1 406 24289 8
16 15 14 13 12
10 9 8 7 6 5 4 3 2 1

British Library Cataloguing in Publication Data
A full catalogue record for this book is available from the British Library.

CONTENTS

CHAPTER 1

ENERGY AND MATTER

Have you ever wondered how birds fly, fish swim, or aliens fly through space? Have you ever thought about why you can walk or run?

These are big questions with many answers. But a good place to start is with energy.

Energy makes everything happen in the universe. One way or another, you use energy in everything you do.

All living things need energy to move, grow, and change. But where do they get the energy? For many living things, food is the main source of energy.

WHAP!

Of course, energy isn't all about eating. Non-living things need energy, too. Energy powers computers and lights houses. Energy from petrol powers lorries, cars, and spaceships.

But what is energy? Scientists say that energy gives the ability to do work. When you push, lift, carry, or pull, you're working.

Work happens when a force moves an object through a distance. It takes work to kick a football. It takes a lot more work to blast a spaceship into space. The more energy something has, the more work it can do.

WAIT!

Energy is found throughout the far reaches of the universe. But the first place to start studying energy is with the tiny things you can't even see.

To understand energy, you must first understand the stuff that makes up everything in the universe. That stuff is matter.

I HAVE A LOT OF MATTER.

Matter is anything that takes up space and has mass. Aliens, people, cars, and just about everything else is made of matter.

THAT CAR HAD MATTER.

SPEED LIMIT 45

Mass is the amount of material in an object. Consider a spaceship and an alien. Both are made of matter, but the spaceship has a lot more mass than the alien.

But where does energy fit in with matter? All matter is made up of tiny particles called atoms. Atoms are made of even smaller particles called neutrons, protons, and electrons.

WHAT DOES THAT ELECTRON CLOUD LOOK LIKE TO YOU?

Protons and neutrons stick together in the atom's centre, called the nucleus. Electrons are in an electron cloud around the nucleus.

You can't see it, but atoms and molecules are never completely still. They're constantly vibrating. All that wiggling and jiggling produces energy.

MOLECULES

Atoms can join together to form groups called molecules. For example, one atom of oxygen and two atoms of hydrogen can combine to form a molecule of water. The atoms in a molecule are held together by energy.

atom tiny particle that is one of the basic building blocks of matter

CHAPTER 2

KINDS OF ENERGY

All the energy in the universe can be placed into two main groups – kinetic energy and potential energy. Kinetic energy is the energy of motion. Anything that moves has kinetic energy. Jiggling atoms, bouncing balls, and dancing aliens all have kinetic energy.

The faster something moves and the more mass it has, the more kinetic energy it has. A big alien has a lot more kinetic energy than a small alien when they run at the same speed.

Potential energy, on the other hand, is stored energy. A spaceship stuck high in a tree has potential energy.

If the spaceship crashes to the ground, its stored energy will be released in a spectacular way.

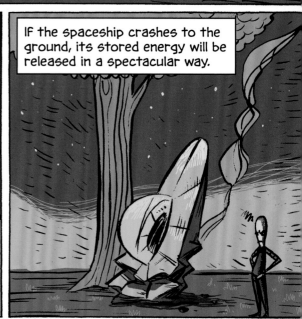

When you stretch a rubber band, you're storing energy as potential energy, too.

If you let go of the stretched rubber band, the potential energy becomes kinetic energy.

kinetic energy the energy of motion
potential energy the stored energy of an object
due to an object's position or what's been done to it

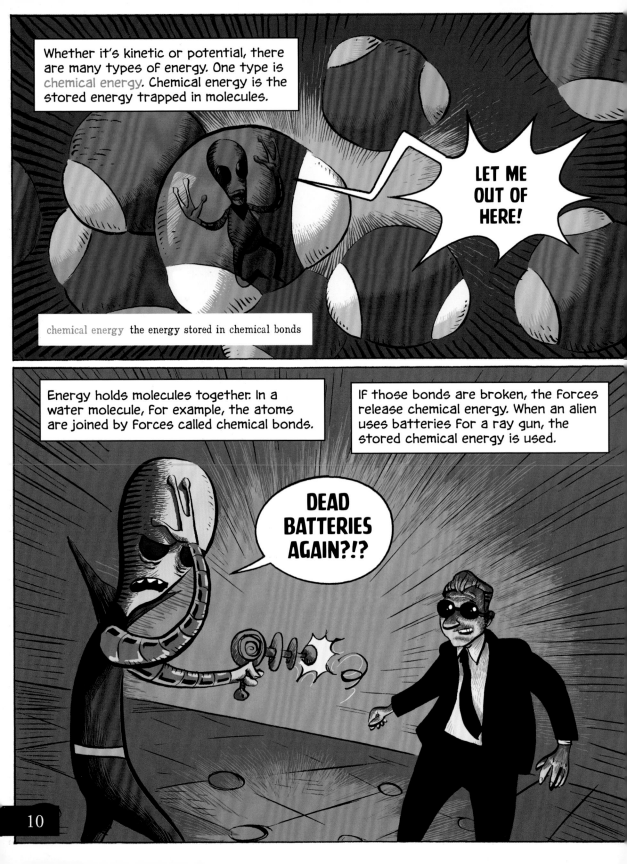

Whether it's kinetic or potential, there are many types of energy. One type is chemical energy. Chemical energy is the stored energy trapped in molecules.

LET ME OUT OF HERE!

chemical energy the energy stored in chemical bonds

Energy holds molecules together. In a water molecule, for example, the atoms are joined by forces called chemical bonds.

If those bonds are broken, the forces release chemical energy. When an alien uses batteries for a ray gun, the stored chemical energy is used.

DEAD BATTERIES AGAIN?!?

Sound is another source of energy that's all around you. Music on the radio, the ticking of a clock, and the bang of a gong all have sound energy.

Sound is produced when the molecules and atoms in an object vibrate. The vibrations make the molecules and atoms hit each other.

The vibrations travel through the air as sound waves. You hear a sound when the vibrations reach your eardrum, causing it to vibrate, too.

IN SPACE, NO ONE CAN HEAR YOU BURP

Sound waves need to travel through some kind of material, such as air, to make sound. Outer space is a vacuum, which means there is no air. So if you burped on the moon, no one would hear it.

Electrons carry electrical energy. An electric current, which is the flow of electrons, carries this type of energy. We use electrical energy to run toasters, lamps, and TVs in our homes.

Power lines carry electrical energy to our homes. But electrical energy can be found in nature, too. Lightning carries a powerful electric current.

ZAP!

electrical energy the form of energy that has a flow of electric charges

We use electrical energy to light our homes, but light itself carries a form of energy. Light, like sound, travels in the form of waves.

Atoms create light when electrons move from higher to lower levels of energy. What we see as light is the energy that's given off from electrons jumping from one level to the other.

The light we see belongs to a family of waves called electromagnetic radiation. These waves can be separated into categories based on their wavelength.

DUDE, THAT COW IS FREAKING ME OUT!

This family includes gamma rays, X-rays, ultraviolet light, visible light, infrared light, microwaves, and radio waves.

Gamma rays have the shortest wavelengths and the highest energy. Radio waves have the longest wavelengths and lowest energy. Visible light is somewhere in the middle.

GAMMA RAY

RADIO WAVE

HOW CAN YOU SEE UV LIGHT?

Visible light is the only form of electromagnetic radiation we can see with our eyes. Some animals, such as butterflies and bees, can also see ultraviolet (UV) light.

BZZZZ?

SOUND VS LIGHT

Sound waves move about 343 metres (1,125 feet) per second. That's fast! But nothing in the universe is faster than light. Light travels an amazing 300,000 kilometres (186,000 miles) per second. That's why you see lightning before you hear thunder.

300,000 KM/SECOND

343 METRES/SECOND

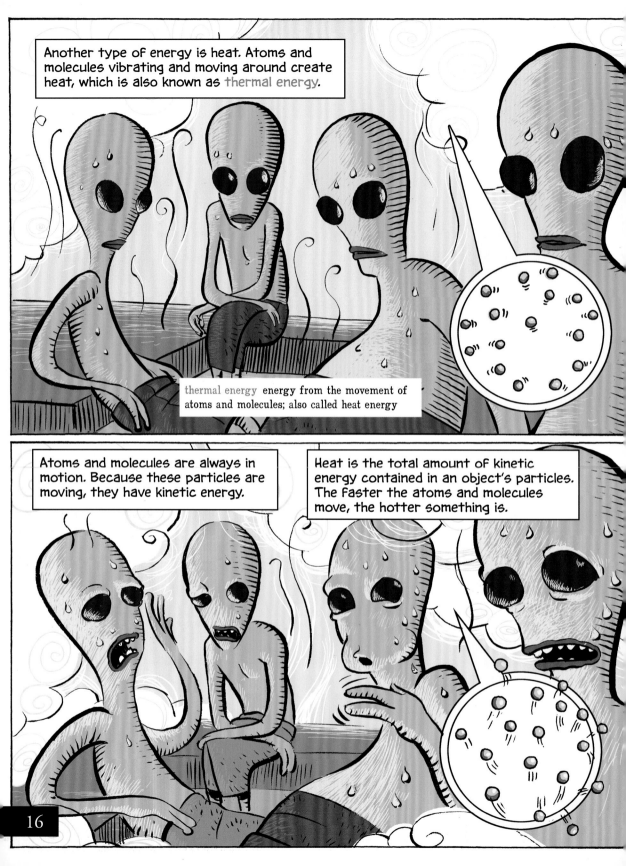

Another type of energy is heat. Atoms and molecules vibrating and moving around create heat, which is also known as thermal energy.

thermal energy energy from the movement of atoms and molecules; also called heat energy

Atoms and molecules are always in motion. Because these particles are moving, they have kinetic energy.

Heat is the total amount of kinetic energy contained in an object's particles. The faster the atoms and molecules move, the hotter something is.

When you take someone's temperature, you're measuring the average kinetic energy of all their particles in motion.

On its own, thermal energy travels from a warmer substance to a cooler substance. For example, suppose you put an ice cube in a glass of water. The heat will flow from the warmer water to the cooler ice until they reach the same temperature.

WHO KEEPS STEALING MY ICE CUBES?!?!

HOT! HOT! HOT!

GEOTHERMAL ENERGY

Geothermal energy is the heat energy inside Earth. It creates hot springs and geysers. It can also be used to heat homes and produce electricity.

CHAPTER 3

CHANGING ENERGY

No matter what kind of energy we're talking about, it can't be created or destroyed. Energy can only be changed from one form to another. You can see this by setting a piece of wood on fire. Wood has stored chemical energy.

The chemical energy in the wood is transformed into heat energy, light energy, and even sound energy when the wood crackles.

Crackle!

Plants can change energy, too. They capture energy from the Sun. Using photosynthesis, they change the energy in sunlight into chemical energy they can store for later needs.

SOAK UP THOSE RAYS, LITTLE BUDDY!

During photosynthesis, plants use the Sun's energy to make food. But not all living things can get energy directly from the Sun.

THIS PHOTOSYNTHESIS THING ISN'T WORKING. I'M STILL HUNGRY!

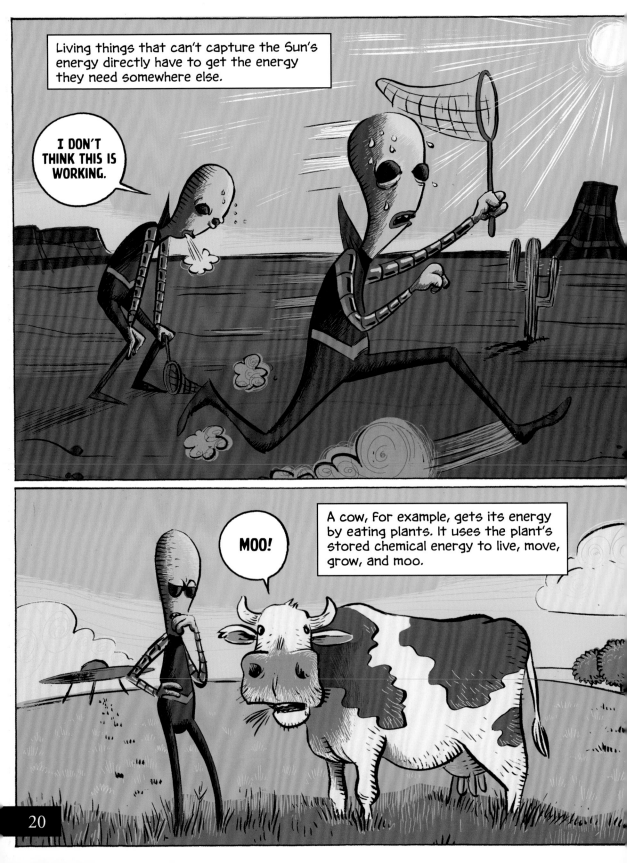

By eating meat, you use an animal's chemical energy to live, move, and grow, too. It also gives you the energy to moo – if you want to, anyway.

MOO?

The simple act of eating is part of a huge energy chain. It takes energy to get energy!

Slurp!

Everything in the universe is part of an energy chain. All things are connected through energy changing forms. Eating is an example of changing energy. So is turning on a torch or a light bulb.

A torch changes stored chemical energy in its batteries into electrical energy. Some of the electrical energy is transferred as light energy when it is turned on.

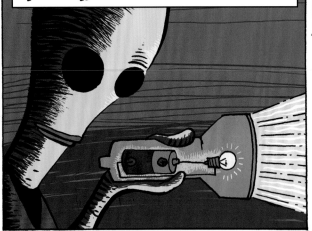

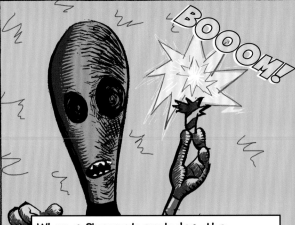

BOOOM!

When a firework explodes, the chemical energy stored within it gets transformed into heat energy, sound energy, and kinetic energy.

But even though energy can change form, it can never be destroyed. This is called the law of conservation of energy. The total amount of energy in each energy chain remains the same.

HE'S CONSERVING ENERGY, ALL RIGHT.

ZZZZZZ

But with each energy conversion, some of the energy becomes unavailable for further use. In each part of an energy chain, some of the energy goes into the environment as thermal energy.

Thermal energy makes things warmer, but it can't be completely changed back into other kinds of energy.

You have to use energy to have things happen. But you never really use up or lose energy. It just goes into another form.

HOT BULB

In some energy transformations, a lot of energy is lost as heat. Only 5 per cent of a typical light bulb's electrical energy provides light. The other 95 per cent is changed into heat.

I THOUGHT LIGHT BULBS ONLY PRODUCED LIGHT!

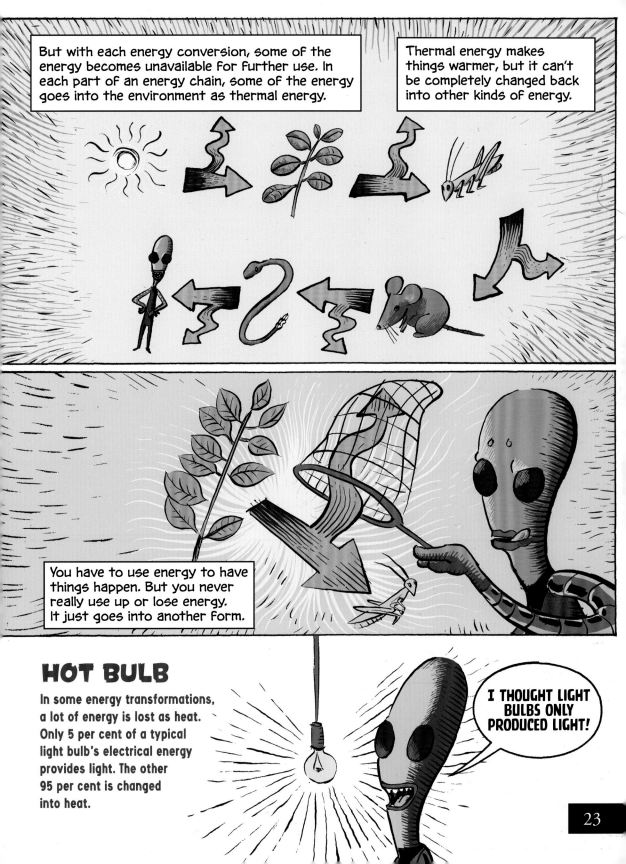

CHAPTER 4

USING AND SAVING ENERGY

But where do we get the energy we use on Earth? Most of it comes from the Sun.

I THINK THE SUN GAVE ME TOO MUCH ENERGY.

I HOPE YOU LIKE YOUR HOT DOGS EXTRA CRISPY!

The Sun creates its own energy by fusing atoms together deep inside its core. The reaction unleashes an incredible amount of heat and light energy.

Only a small fraction of this energy reaches Earth. But what does reach the surface warms the planet and allows life to exist. If it weren't for the Sun, we wouldn't be here.

We can also use the Sun's energy directly. The Sun's energy can power solar panels and solar cells.

NUCLEAR ENERGY

Mass itself contains energy. The mass in the nucleus of atoms is the source of nuclear energy. There's a huge amount of energy holding the nucleus of an atom together. Nuclear energy is released when nuclei are broken apart or fused together. In nuclear power plants, energy is released when an atom's nucleus is split apart. In the Sun, nuclear energy is produced when atomic nuclei are joined together.

The Sun is also the reason we have fossil fuels, such as oil, coal, and natural gas. Fossil fuels are formed from the ancient remains of plants and animals, which once used the Sun for energy as well.

TOO ... HEAVY ...

LOOKS LIKE HE'LL END UP AS A FOSSIL FUEL.

People depend on fossil fuels for energy. Most power plants burn fossil fuels for energy. For example, coal is burned to make electricity.

Burning coal heats water into steam. The high-pressure steam turns turbines, which drive generators to produce electricity. The electricity is then sent through electric cables to power communities and spaceships.

Unfortunately, burning fossil fuels causes pollution and other environmental problems.

There is also a limited supply of fossil fuels. It takes millions of years to create fossil fuels.

But the Sun will keep shining and releasing energy for at least a few billion years more. That's one reason why scientists are looking at better ways to harness its energy.

It takes time to come up with efficient ways to use renewable sources of energy. That's why it's important to conserve energy where and when we can.

You're conserving energy each time you reuse or recycle paper, plastic, and metal.

GLASS

ALUMINIUM

PAPER

SPACESHIPS

Using public transport saves more energy than driving cars separately.

BUS STOP

More than half of the energy used in the home by people in the UK is for heating rooms. Turning down the thermostat can help save energy.

Swapping inefficient light bulbs with energy-efficient ones also helps save energy.

But there's a lot more to energy than saving fossil fuels. Energy is an important part of the universe. And life — alien or otherwise — couldn't exist without it.

GLOSSARY

atom tiny particle that is a basic building block of matter

chemical energy the energy stored in chemical bonds

electrical energy the form of energy that has a flow of electric charges

kinetic energy the energy of a moving object

molecule group of two or more atoms linked together

nuclear energy energy contained in the nucleus of an atom

potential energy the stored energy of an object

radiation a form of energy, such as heat, light, X-rays, microwaves, or radio waves. Radiation also includes dangerous, high-energy nuclear radiation.

thermal energy energy from the movement of atoms and molecules; also called heat energy

wavelength the distance between two peaks of a wave

FIND OUT MORE

BOOKS

Electrical Experiments: Electricity and Circuits (Do It Yourself), Rachel Lynette (Heinemann Library, 2008)

Forms of Energy (Sci-Hi), Anna Claybourne (Raintree, 2010)

The Scientists Behind Energy (Sci-Hi), Andrew Solway (Raintree, 2012)

The Shocking World of Electricity with Max Axiom, Super Scientist (Graphic Science), Liam O'Donnell (Raintree, 2011)

WEBSITES

energyquest.ca.gov/movieroom/index.html
The "Movie Room" of the California Energy Commission education website has a range of clear and informative videos to choose from.

www.energysavingtrust.org.uk
Go to this website for advice about how to save energy and money.

www.sciencemuseum.org.uk/on-line/energy/site/quiz0.asp
Explore how energy powers every aspect of your life, where it comes from, and how the planet is coping. There are stories, games, quizzes, and videos about energy on this Science Museum website.

www.switchedonkids.org.uk
This website has quizzes, games, and information about electricity and how to use it safely.

INDEX